You're My Hero,

A FAWCETT CREST BOOK
Fawcett Publications, Inc., Greenwich, Conn.
Member of American Book Publishers Council, Inc.

— Charlie Brown!

Selected Cartoons from PEANUTS EVERY SUNDAY VOL.2

by CHARLES M. SCHULZ

Other Peanuts Books in Fawcett Crest Editions:

This book, prepared especially for Fawcett Publications, Inc., comprises the second half of PEANUTS EVERY SUNDAY, and is reprinted by arrangement with Holt, Rinehart and Winston, Inc.

Third Fawcett Crest Printing, December 1968

Published by Fawcett World Library
67 West 44th Street, New York, N. Y. 10036
Printed in the United States of America

CLOMP!

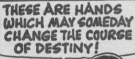

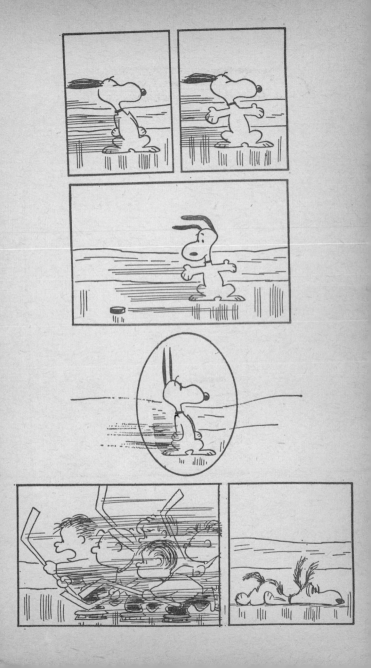

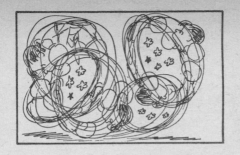

✧ POW! WHAM! ✧

BANG
WHAP! POW!
SOCKO!
OUCH! OOF!
LEGGO!
YIPE!

I CAN'T GET THAT STUPID KITE IN THE AIR! I CAN'T! I CAN'T!

OH, COME ON NOW, CHARLIE BROWN...THAT'S NO WAY TO TALK...

THE WHOLE TROUBLE WITH YOU IS YOU DON'T BELIEVE IN YOURSELF! YOU DON'T BELIEVE IN YOUR OWN ABILITIES!

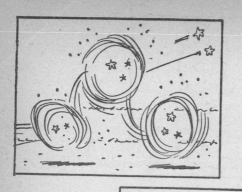

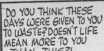

IT ALWAYS COMES AS A SHOCK WHEN IT HAPPENS TO SOMEONE YOU KNOW...

DO YOU WANNA SEE A KID WITH A GREAT THROWING ARM?

WHAT A STRUGGLE...IT TOOK ME FORTY-FIVE MINUTES TO LAND HIM!

SKRITCH
SKRITCH
SKRITCH

SKRITCH SKRITCH
SKRITCH
SKRITCH
SKRITCH

SIGH

WHAT DO YOU HAVE THERE, CHARLIE BROWN?

I'VE WRITTEN A POEM..

REALLY? READ IT..

ALL RIGHT.. IT ISN'T VERY LONG..

SOME DAYS YOU THINK MAYBE YOU KNOW EVERYTHING...SOME DAYS YOU THINK MAYBE YOU DON'T KNOW ANYTHING... SOME DAYS YOU THINK YOU KNOW A FEW THINGS...SOME DAYS YOU DON'T EVEN KNOW HOW OLD YOU ARE.

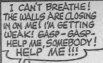

I'VE LOST IT, CHARLIE BROWN! I'M JUST NOT THE FUSSBUDGET I USED TO BE! I JUST CAN'T DO IT ANY MORE! I USED TO BE ABLE TO FUSS FOR HOURS...NOW I GET TIRED

I DON'T HAVE ANY VOLUME, I DON'T HAVE ANY TONE, I DON'T HAVE THE FEEL OF IT ANY MORE.. I'VE LOST IT! I'VE LOST IT! IT'S GONE!

IT'S KIND OF SAD TO SEE A GREAT TALENT LIKE THAT DETERIORATE

I GUESS THAT'S JUST ONE OF THOSE THINGS THAT HAPPEN, THOUGH.. ESPECIALLY IN A CREATIVE FIELD!

I DON'T WANNA TAKE A NAP! I WANNA PLAY OUTSIDE!!!

I GOT IT LICKED NOW CHARLIE BROWN! I GOT IT LICKED!

FROM NOW ON I USE A 'THROAT-MIKE'!

PERHAPS YOU SHOULD SEE A DOCTOR...

THIS IS A SCULPTURE WHICH STANDS IN THE LITTLE GARDEN JUST BEHIND THE HOUSE..

HERE I AM AGAIN POSING BY THE HOUSE

WILL THESE PICTURES BE WORTH A LOT OF MONEY SOMEDAY?

I DOUBT IT..

I DON'T SEE HOW ANYBODY CAN SAVE SOMETHING THAT WON'T BE WORTH A LOT OF MONEY SOMEDAY..

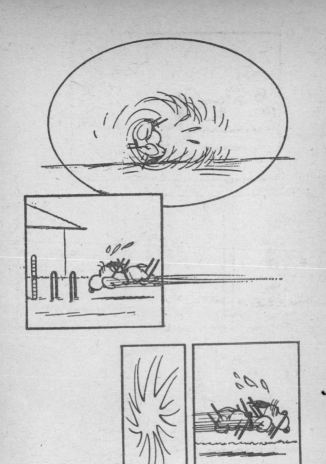

And don't forget about all the other PEANUTS books in the new Fawcett Crest editions. Good Grief! More than 26 million of them in paperback!

© 1967 United Feature Syndicate, Inc.

D1097	WHO DO YOU THINK YOU ARE, CHARLIE BROWN?	**D1129**	GOOD GRIEF, CHARLIE BROWN
D1070	GOOD OL' SNOOPY	**D1128**	HEY, PEANUTS!
D1142	VERY FUNNY, CHARLIE BROWN	**D1115**	THE WONDERFUL WORLD OF PEANUTS
D1140	WHAT NEXT, CHARLIE BROWN!	**D1113**	HERE COMES CHARLIE BROWN
D1134	YOU ARE TOO MUCH, CHARLIE BROWN	**D1105**	WE'RE ON YOUR SIDE, CHARLIE BROWN
D1141	FOR THE LOVE OF PEANUTS!	**D1099**	HERE COMES SNOOPY
D1130	YOU'RE A WINNER, CHARLIE BROWN	**D1096**	LET'S FACE IT, CHARLIE BROWN
	D1133 FUN WITH PEANUTS		

Wherever Paperbacks Are Sold